Dear Parents,

Welcome to the Magic School Bus!

For over 20 years, teachers, parents, and children have been enchanted and inspired by Ms. Frizzle and the fabulous cast of beloved characters that make up The Magic School Bus series.

The unusual field trips, visual jokes, eye-catching details, and interesting information are just a few of the elements that make The Magic School Bus series an excellent tool to get your child excited about school, reading, and exploring their world.

It is important that children learn to read well enough to succeed in school and beyond. Here are some ideas for reading this book with your child:

- Look at the book together. Encourage your child to read the title and make a prediction about the story.
- Read the book together. Encourage your child to sound out words when appropriate. When your child struggles, you can help by providing the word.
- Encourage your child to retell the story. This is a great way to check for comprehension.

Enjoy the experience of helping your child learn to read and love to read!

Visit www.scholastic.com/magicschoolbus to subscribe to Scholastic's free parent e-newsletter, and find book lists, read-aloud tips, and learning hints for pre-readers, beginners, and older kids, too. Inspire a love of books in your child!

There are many Magic School Bus books for your reader to enjoy. We think you will enjoy these, too:

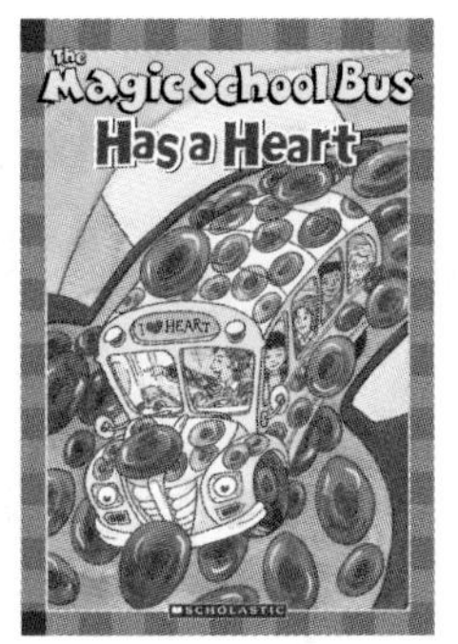

Written by Kristin Earhart
Illustrated by Carolyn Bracken

Based on The Magic School Bus ® books
written by Joanna Cole and illustrated by Bruce Degen

The author and editor would like to thank Dr. Joel Bish, Professor of Neuroscience and Psychology, Ursinus College, and Owen Bish, Junior Advisor, for their expert advice in preparing the manuscript and illustrations.

ISBN-13: 978-0-545-16726-0
ISBN-10: 0-545-16726-4

12 11 10 9 8 7 6 5 4 3 2 1 9 10 11 12 13 14/0

Designed by Rick DeMonico

Printed in the U.S.A.

First printing, September 2009

The Magic School Bus®
Comes to Its Senses

Arnold Ralphie Keesha Phoebe Carlos Tim Wanda Dorothy Ann

SCHOLASTIC INC.

New York Toronto London Auckland
Sydney Mexico City New Delhi Hong Kong

It's fun to be in Ms. Frizzle's class.
We see and hear some very strange things.
GOOD MORNING
SWEET
SOUR
BITTER
UNSWEETENED CHOCOLATE
SALTY
PRETZEL
SALT

Arnold
TOUCH
SOMETIMES WE DON'T BELIEVE OUR EYES!
OR EARS!
3-D

We are learning about senses.
Phoebe says, "Taste is my favorite sense."
5 SENSES
SEE
HEAR
TOUCH
SMELL
TASTE
TOUCH
DA
TASTE
LIMA BEANS ARE MY FAVORITE THING TO TASTE.
LIMA BEANS?
MAKING SENSE
by Phoebe
People have five senses.
We see, hear, feel, taste,
and smell.
Our senses tell us about the
world around us.

Ms. Frizzle tells us we are going on a trip.
"To the bus, kids!" she says.

We follow the Friz to the bus.
Wanda asks, “Will this trip be normal?”
“Ms. Frizzle’s trips are never normal,” says Arnold.
I SMELL SOMETHING FISHY.

TODAY'S MENU
FISHSTICKS
PEAS & CARROTS
COTTAGE CHEESE
FRUIT
IT'S THE SCHOOL LUNCHROOM.

We drive to an apple orchard.
We see a family having a picnic.
All at once, our bus starts to shrink.
MACINTOS
IT'S TIME TO START OUR SENSES GAME.
I SENSE THAT THIS IS NOT A NORMAL FIELD TRIP.
HEAR THIS
LISTEN

Ms. Frizzle has a stack of cards.
Each card has a clue about one of the five senses.
We read them to play the clue game.
RED DELICIOUS
ROME BEAUTY

Just then, we hear a loud buzzing sound.
A bee is chasing our bus!
We zoom toward the little girl for cover.
Keesha reads the first clue for our game.
"No matter what you hear,
the sound starts in your ________."

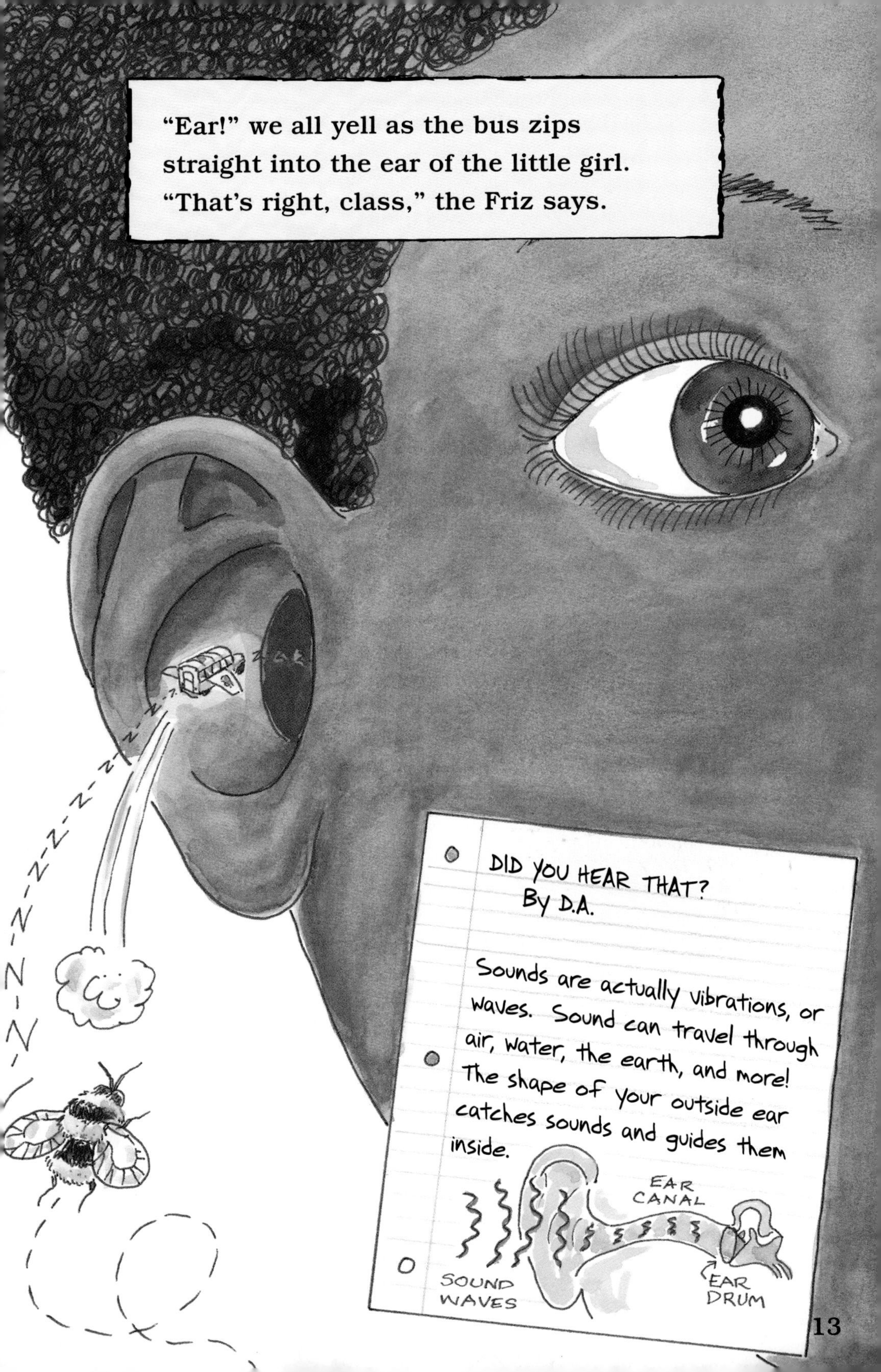
"Ear!" we all yell as the bus zips straight into the ear of the little girl. "That's right, class," the Friz says.
DID YOU HEAR THAT?
By D.A.
Sounds are actually vibrations, or waves. Sound can travel through air, water, the earth, and more! The shape of your outside ear catches sounds and guides them inside.
EAR CANAL
SOUND WAVES
EAR DRUM

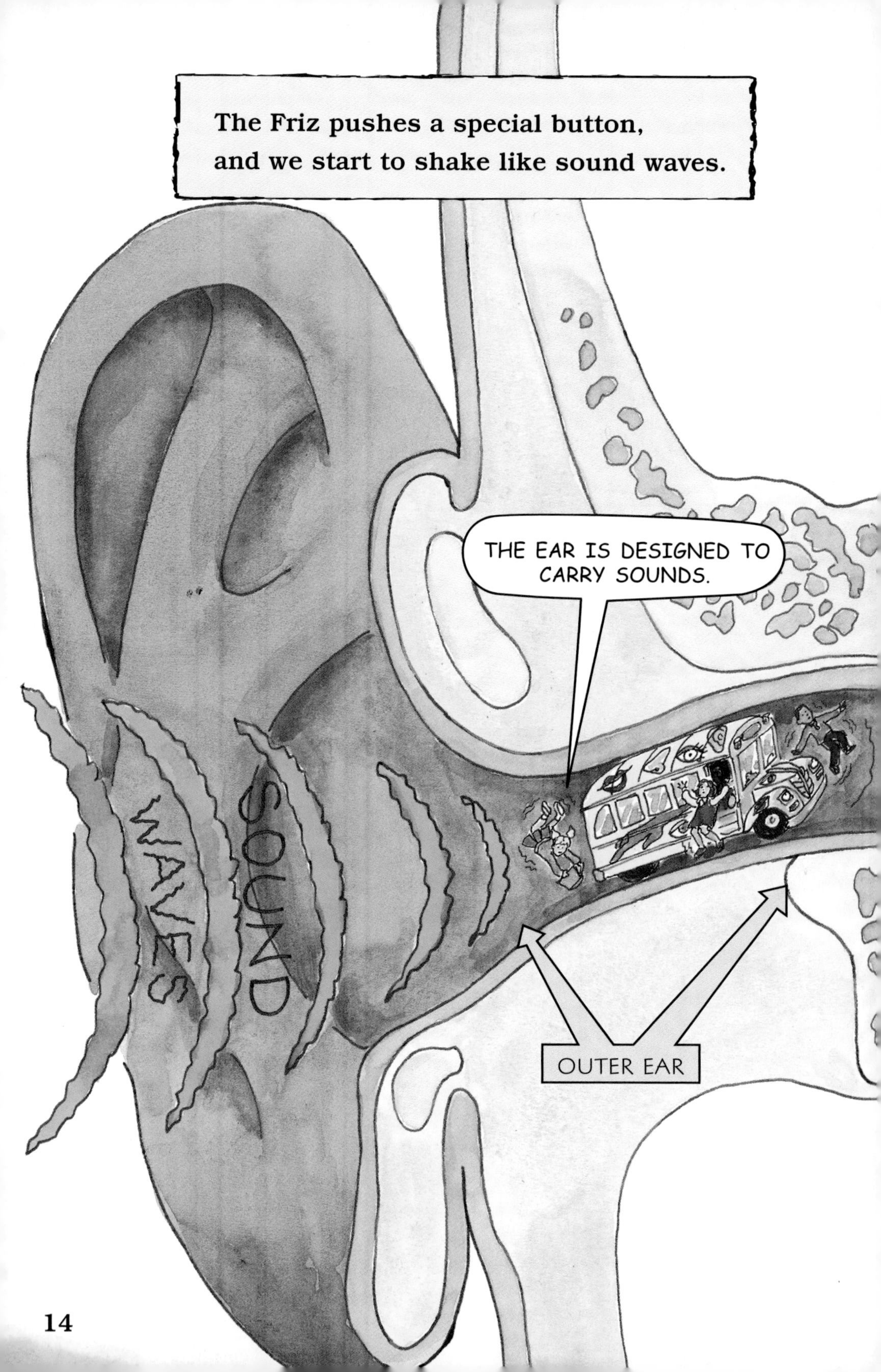
The Friz pushes a special button,
and we start to shake like sound waves.
THE EAR IS DESIGNED TO CARRY SOUNDS.
SOUND WAVES
OUTER EAR

We shake right out of the bus and through a thin piece of skin.
"Kids, that was the eardrum," the Friz says.
"Here is the next clue:
When you hear a drop of rain,
You really hear it in your __________."

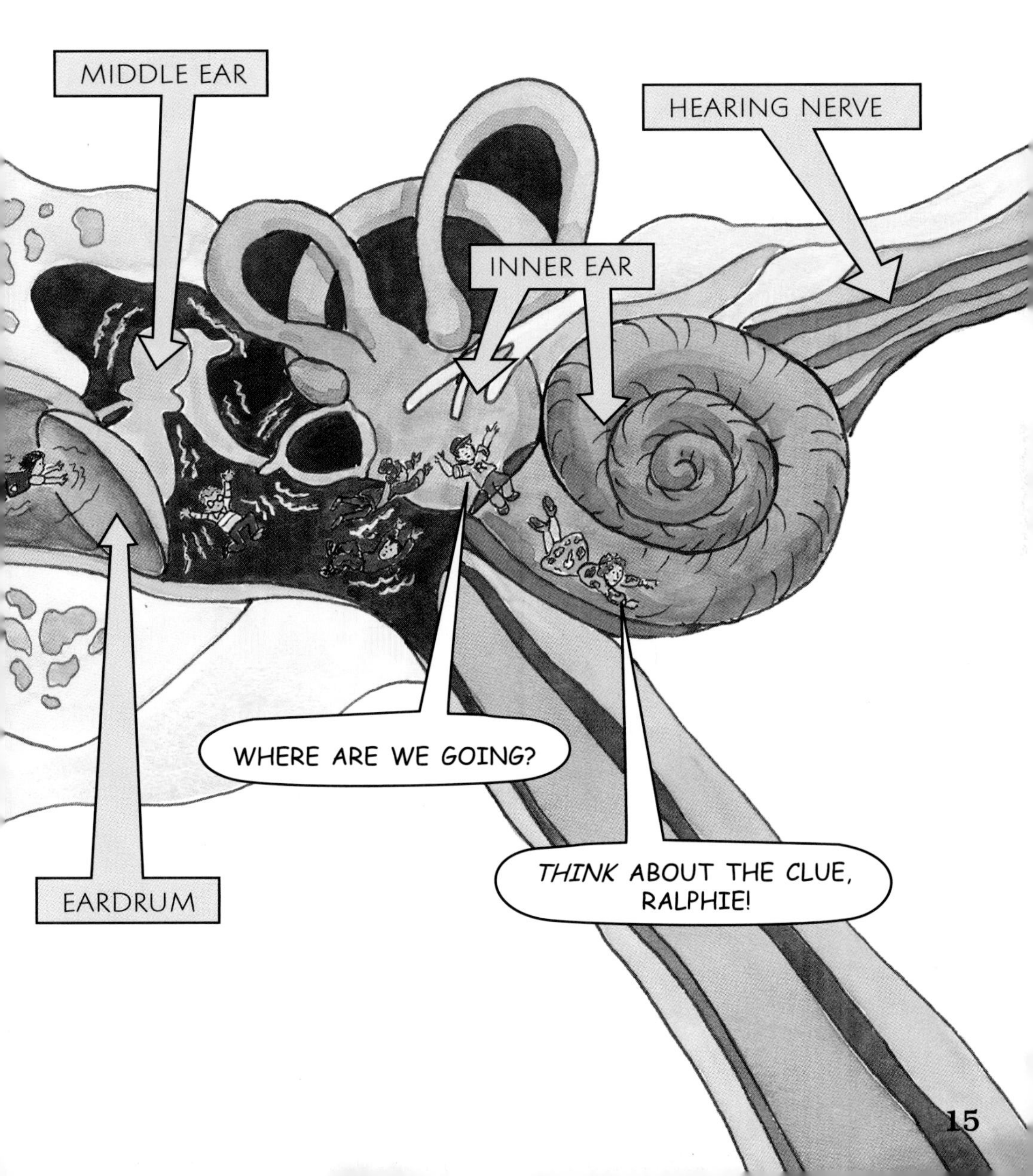

Before we can answer the clue, we start to spin through the inner ear. In a flash, we are zipping along the hearing nerve on our way to the brain!

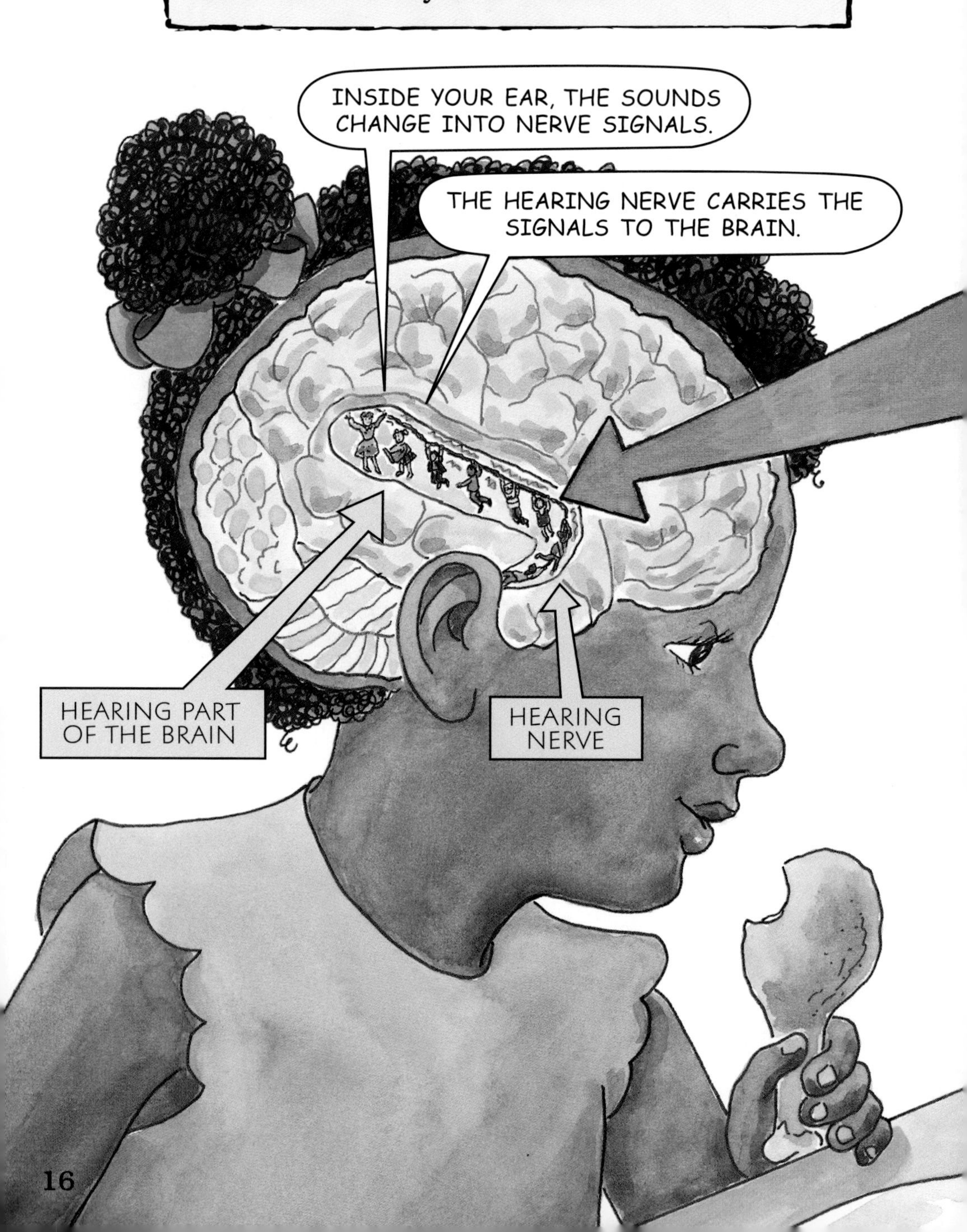

THE **BRAIN** IS THE ANSWER TO OUR CLUE!
THE BRAIN MAKES SENSE OF ALL THE SIGNALS.
THAT BUS WILL NEVER MAKE SENSE TO ME.

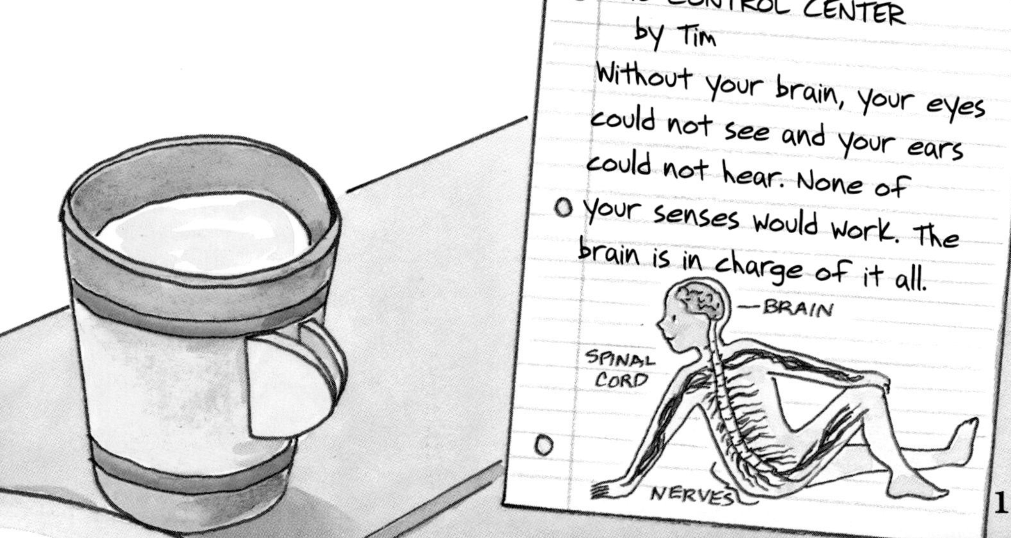
THE CONTROL CENTER
by Tim
Without your brain, your eyes could not see and your ears could not hear. None of your senses would work. The brain is in charge of it all.
BRAIN
SPINAL CORD
NERVES

We land in the hearing center in the brain.
"Let's look around," Ms. Frizzle says.
We head for the vision center.
I WANT YOU TO SEE SOMETHING. . . .
I'VE NEVER SEEN ANYTHING LIKE THIS!
HEARING CENTER
VISION CENTER

When we reach the vision center,
signals are coming from the eye.
The brain tells the girl what her eyes are seeing.
"Hop on, kids!" the Friz says from the bus.
THE SEEING NERVE CARRIES SIGNALS FROM THE EYE TO THE BRAIN.
RIGHT NOW IT IS CARRYING A BUSLOAD OF KIDS.
THAT TAKES A LOT OF NERVE.

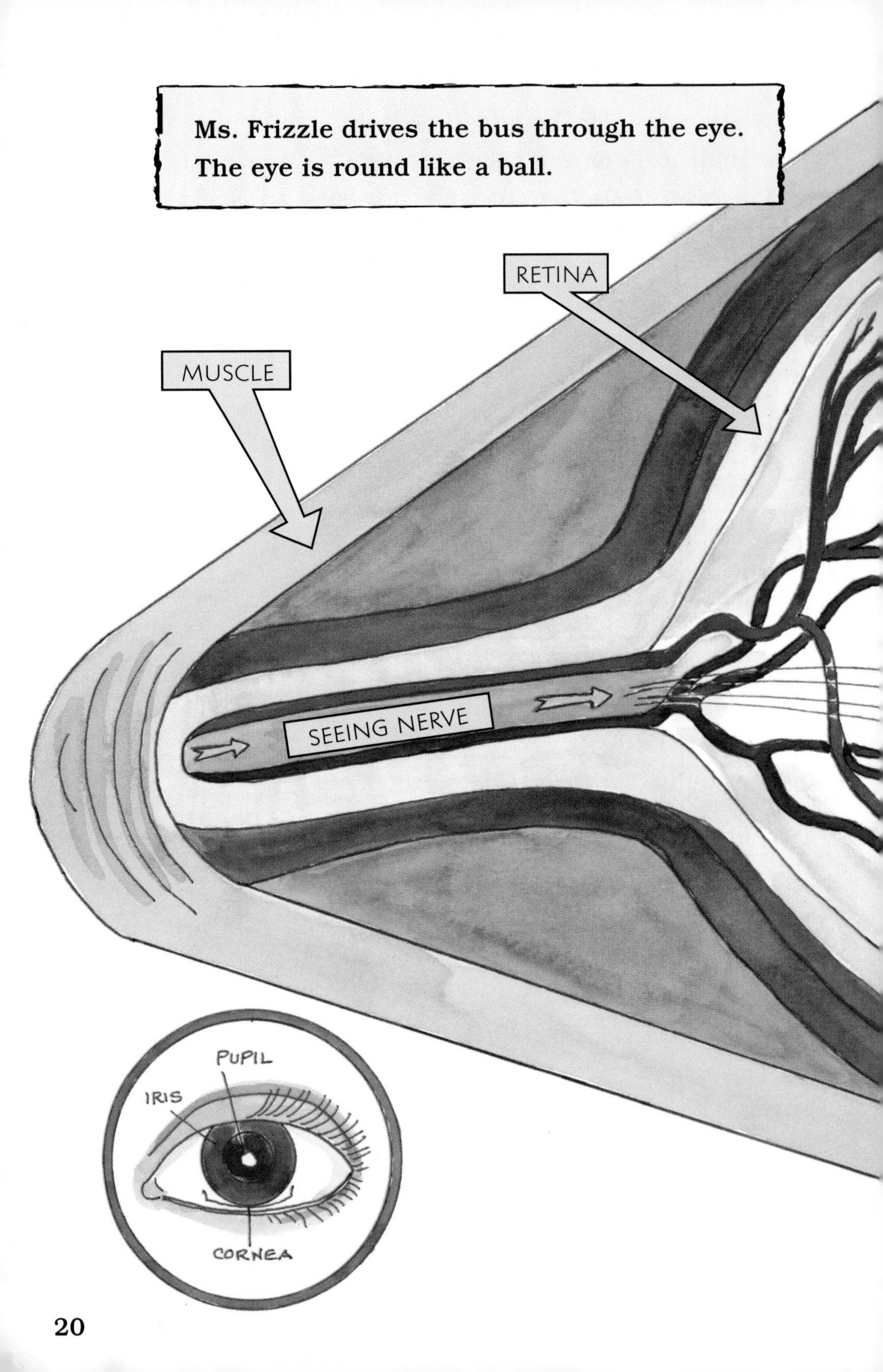
Ms. Frizzle drives the bus through the eye.
The eye is round like a ball.
RETINA
MUSCLE
SEEING NERVE
PUPIL
IRIS
CORNEA

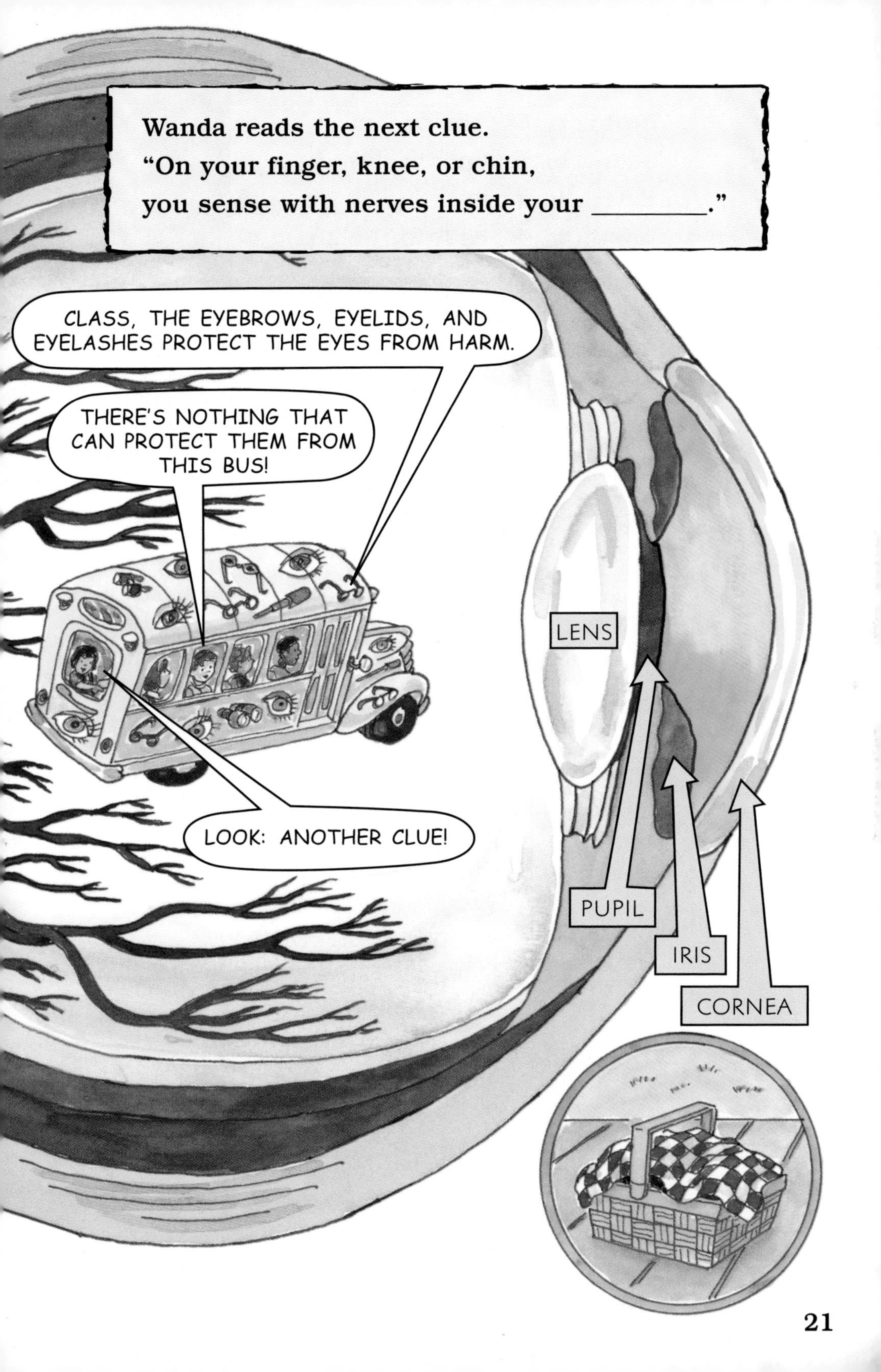
Wanda reads the next clue.
"On your finger, knee, or chin,
you sense with nerves inside your ________."
CLASS, THE EYEBROWS, EYELIDS, AND EYELASHES PROTECT THE EYES FROM HARM.
THERE'S NOTHING THAT CAN PROTECT THEM FROM THIS BUS!
LOOK: ANOTHER CLUE!
LENS
PUPIL
IRIS
CORNEA

We whiz out of the eye.
We land in a picnic basket.
It's dark in here!
Something oozes into the bus.

MY TOUCH NERVES FEEL SOMETHING GOOEY!

IT FEELS YUCKY.

BUT IT SMELLS DELICIOUS. . . .

We sit in the dark and think about the clue.
"Skin!" D.A. finally yells.
"We sense with the nerves in our *skin*!"
Then the basket lid opens.
We landed in an apple pie!
WOW!
ALL THE PIE YOU CAN EAT.

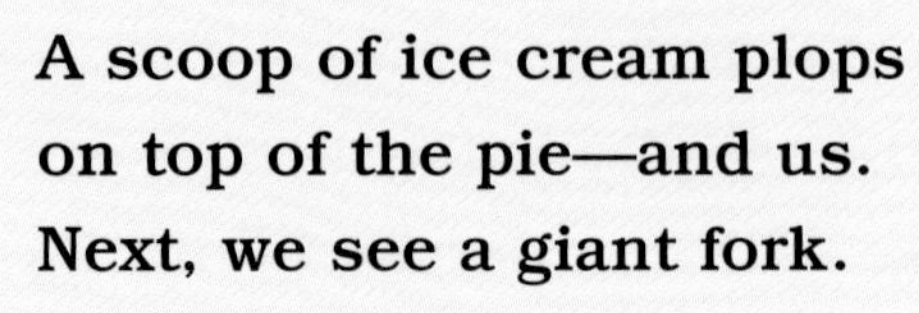
A scoop of ice cream plops on top of the pie—and us. Next, we see a giant fork.

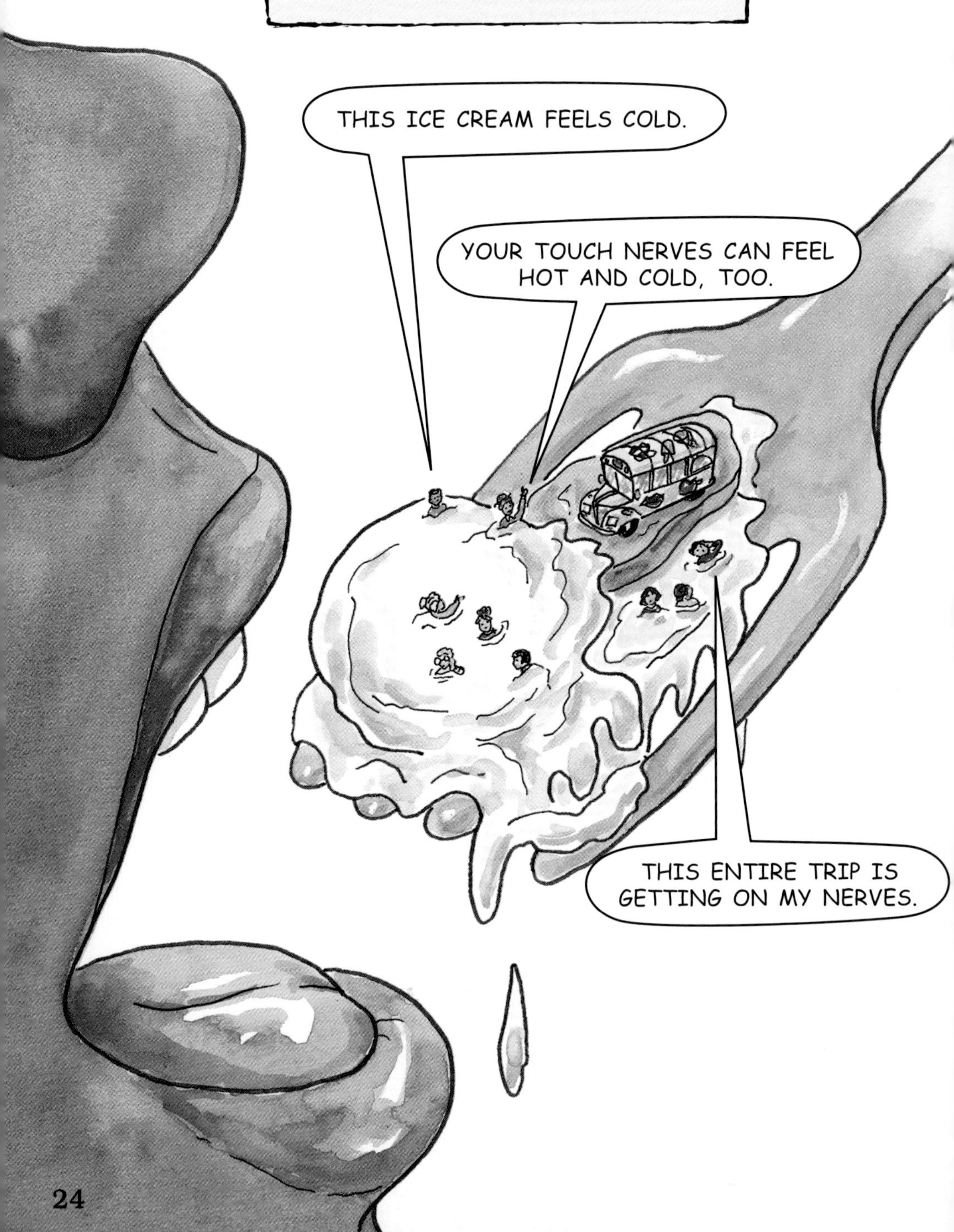
THIS ICE CREAM FEELS COLD.
YOUR TOUCH NERVES CAN FEEL HOT AND COLD, TOO.
THIS ENTIRE TRIP IS GETTING ON MY NERVES.

The fork lifts us up.
Now we are inside the girl's mouth!
Tim reads our next clue.
"Whether you are old or young,
you use the taste buds on your ________."
NOSE
TEETH
TONGUE
FOOD
WE ARE ON HER TONGUE!
WATCH OUT FOR HER TEETH!
APPLE PIE

"The answer is tongue!" says Carlos.
"Are the taste buds in these bumps?"
"That's right, Carlos!" the Friz says.
TEETH
THE TASTE BUDS TELL THE BRAIN THAT THE PIE IS SWEET.
SHE'S GOING TO SWALLOW US!
THAT DOESN'T SEEM VERY SWEET TO ME.
TASTE BUDS
TONGUE
NERVES
TEETH

We are in the back of the throat.
The girl is about to swallow!
Suddenly, we float up. Phew!
The Friz gives us some special goggles.
We see the tiny smell bits all around us.
THESE SMELL BITS ARE SUPER SMALL.
THE BITS MAKE THINGS SMELL THE WAY THEY DO.
TONGUE
FOOD
THE SECRET PASSAGE
by Wanda
Your mouth and nose are connected, so the smells from food can float up to your nose. Your sense of smell gives food more taste.

Soon, we are in the nose.
We want to get out of here!
D.A. reads the next clue:
"You don't need to make a fuss.
Everyone, get on __________."
MY SENSES TELL ME TO LEAVE!
LET'S READ THE LAST CLUE.
NOSE HAIRS KEEP THE AIRWAY CLEAN
SMELL CENTER IN THE BRAIN
SMELL CELLS
SMELL MOLECULES

"THE BUS!" we all cry.
Just then, we hear a friendly honk.
The next thing we know . . .
HOP ON!
BEEP!
BEEP!

We are back at school.
Our class is sitting on a soft blanket.
We are having a picnic.
All of our senses are going strong!
They always are with Ms. Frizzle!
LUNCH
I'VE NEVER *FELT* BETTER.

LOOK AT MS. FRIZZLE'S DRESS!
IT'S BUGGING ME!

WILD ANIMAL FACTS

A dog's nose can smell 40 times
better than a person's nose.
A bloodhound has long ears
that stir up smells on the ground.

An eagle can spot food
from a mile above the ground.

Cats can hear sounds
that humans cannot hear at all.

WHAT DOES AN ANT SMELL LIKE?

DELICIOUS!

ANTEATER MASK